My little **green** book of

stories and pictures

*45 New Testament stories
and activities
for young children*

© Scripture Union 2011
First published 2011
ISBN 978 1 84427 636 3
Material also available as A4 photocopiable group resource
Stories and Pictures New Testament, first published 2011

Scripture Union
207–209 Queensway, Bletchley, Milton Keynes, MK2 2EB
Email: info@scriptureunion.org.uk
Website: www.scriptureunion.org.uk

Scripture Union Australia
Locked Bag 2, Central Coast Business Centre, NSW 2252
Website: www.scriptureunion.org.au

Scripture Union USA
PO Box 987, Valley Forge, PA 19482
Website: www.scriptureunion.org

Scripture quotations are from the Contemporary English Version published by HarperCollinsPublishers © 1991, 1992, 1995 American Bible Society.

Children's retellings of Bible stories previously published in The Big Bible Storybook, © Scripture Union 2006.

British Library Cataloguing-in-Publication Data
A catalogue record of this book is available from the British Library.

Printed and bound in Singapore by Tien Wah Press

Cover and internal design: kwgraphicdesign
Cover photography: Steve Shipman
Illustrations: Sonia Canals
Tiddlywinks series editor: Maggie Barfield
Writer: Maggie Barfield
Freelance editor and project manager: Louise Titley

🌱 Scripture Union is an international charity working with churches in more than 130 countries, providing resources to bring the good news of Jesus Christ to children, young people and families and to encourage them to develop spiritually through the Bible and prayer.

As well as our network of volunteers, staff and associates who run holidays, church-based events and school Christian groups, we produce a wide range of publications and support those who use our resources through training programmes.

Contents

How to use this book

All the activities in this book can be used to introduce your child to a Bible story, or to remind them of a Bible story that you have just shared together and to get them involved in more of the detail. Each picture activity is designed to stimulate further thought on, and discussion of, the Bible story at the level of under-5s, as well as to provide them with plenty of fun!

Before you start, read through the notes to check you have all the art materials you need. Most of the activities need only crayons, paints, glue and collage materials, but some of them do use some less everyday art materials to get particular effects.

Have fun! Your relationship with your child can tell them as much about God's love for them as the retelling of a Bible story.

Why not read the story from the Bible yourself before you start, to remind yourself of the details?

A taster verse or two of the actual Bible text is also given. You could use this to help your child relate the Bible stories to a complete Bible. Try looking up the verse in your Bible and showing your child the same words on the Bible page. (All actual Bible text used here comes from the CEV translation.)

Tell the story. The retelling of each Bible story has been written in a way that is accessible to under-5s.

Jesus feeds many people

Read it from the Bible
Matthew 15:32–39

"His disciples said, "This place is like a desert. Where can we find enough food to feed such a crowd?"
Matthew 15:33

Tell the story
Lots of people come to see Jesus. They came to hear the stories Jesus told. They came to see him make sick people well again.

Everyone loved to be with Jesus. No one wanted to go home. They stayed there for one day, two days, then three days. Soon, they had eaten all the food they had brought with them. And soon after that, they began to feel very hungry!

Jesus cared for the people. Jesus knew that they needed food to eat. Jesus' friends had seven loaves of bread and a few fish.

Jesus said, "Thank you," to God for the bread and fish. Then he gave the food to all the people! Lots and lots of people!

And everyone had something to eat. The people could hardly believe it. But they knew they did not have hungry tummies any more.

Just seven loaves of bread and a few fish fed all those people – thanks to Jesus!

Talk to God
Thank you, Jesus, that you know what people need and look after them. Thank you for looking after us.

Use the picture
1 You can use the picture as an introduction to the Bible story or to help you review the story together.

2 Explain that you are each going to make a picture about the Bible story. Then you are going to use the pictures to make a book about Jesus.

3 Give each child a copy of the picture and read the heading 'Jesus feeds people'. Let the children colour or paint the picture. As they work, chat about the Bible story. Can the children tell you what happened? Who was hungry? Did they have much food? Could Jesus help? What did Jesus do? What did the people do? How do the children feel about Jesus?

Talk to God. Each activity is rounded off with the words of a prayer or an idea for a prayer topic.

Use the picture! Each activity gives you ideas on how to get the most from each Bible picture, stimulating further exploration of the story.

A message for Mary

Read it from the Bible

Luke 1:26–56

'Then the angel told Mary, "Don't be afraid! God is pleased with you, and you will have a son. His name will be Jesus."' *Luke 1:30–31*

Tell the story

Mary was busy at her house. She was soon going to be married to Joseph and there was so much to do. Mary was very excited about the wedding.

Suddenly, she looked up. An angel was standing there. Mary was surprised. She had never seen an angel before.

"Don't be frightened, Mary," the angel said. "I have brought you an important message. God has chosen you to have a very special baby. The baby boy will be God's own Son."

Mary was puzzled. "But what about our wedding?" she asked.

The angel smiled. "Don't worry. God knows all about it," he said. Then the angel disappeared.

Mary thought about the message the angel had brought. God's Son would soon be born, and she had been chosen to be his mother. How amazing! Mary sang happily as she worked. What would Joseph say when he heard her news?

Talk to God

Thank you, God, that Mary trusted you and was happy when you spoke to her. Help us to trust you too.

Use the picture

1 You can use the picture as an introduction to the Bible story or to help you review the story together.

2 There are five Bible-story pictures to go with this series about 'Christmas people', each showing characters who were affected by the news of the coming of Jesus. As the first picture is completed (coloured, painted or collaged), keep it to make a long frieze of the whole story.

Jesus is born

Read it from the Bible

Luke 2:1–7

'Mary was engaged to Joseph and travelled with him to Bethlehem. She was soon going to have a baby, and while they were there, she gave birth to her firstborn son.' *Luke 2:5–7*

Tell the story

Mary and Joseph were very excited. It was nearly time for Mary to have her baby. But Mary could not have her baby at home. Mary and Joseph had to leave their house and travel a long way to a town called Bethlehem. When they got there, Bethlehem was full of people. Joseph and Mary looked for a place to stay. But everywhere was already full of people. No room here. No room there. What were they going to do?

A kind man said that Mary and Joseph could stay in the stable by his house. This was where the animals lived. Mary and Joseph were very pleased to have somewhere to stay at last.

Very soon, baby Jesus was born. Mary wrapped him up to keep him warm. Joseph made a soft bed for him in the hay. Mary and Joseph were very excited. Jesus had been born!

Talk to God

Thank you, God, for the wonderful gift of your Son, Jesus, at Christmas time.

Use the picture

1 You can use the picture as an introduction to the Bible story or to help you review the story together.

2 There are five Bible-story pictures to go with this series about 'Christmas people', each showing characters who were affected by the news of the coming of Jesus. As the second picture is completed (coloured, painted or collaged), tape it to the first scene ('A message for Mary') and keep it to make a long frieze of the whole story.

Jesus is born Luke 2:1–7

A message for the shepherds

Read it from the Bible

Luke 2:8–21

'All at once an angel came down to them from the Lord, and the brightness of the Lord's glory flashed around them. The shepherds were frightened. But the angel said, "Don't be afraid! I have good news for you, which will make everyone happy."' *Luke 2:9–10*

Tell the story

One night, some shepherds were on the hillside outside Bethlehem. Suddenly, there was a dazzling light and an angel appeared. The shepherds were very scared. "Don't be frightened," the angel said. "I have brought you some wonderful news. God's Son has been born tonight."

Lots more angels appeared in the sky. They sang, "Praise to God in heaven. Peace to everyone on earth."

When the angels had gone, the shepherds said to each other, "Come on, let's go and find this special baby." They left their sheep. They ran down the hillside to Bethlehem. They found baby Jesus lying on a bed of straw, just as the angels had said. The shepherds told Mary and Joseph all about the angel's message.

The shepherds were so excited they told everyone they met the good news, "God's Son has been born!"

Talk to God

Thank you, God, that you wanted everyone to know about Jesus!

Use the picture

1 You can use the picture as an introduction to the Bible story or to help you review the story together.

2 There are five Bible-story pictures to go with this series about 'Christmas people', each showing characters who were affected by the news of the coming of Jesus. As the third picture is completed (coloured, painted or collaged), tape it to the other scenes ('A message for Mary', 'Jesus is born') and keep it to make a long frieze of the whole story.

A message for the shepherds Luke 2:8–21

Simeon and Anna

Read it from the Bible

Luke 2:22–38

'At this time a man named Simeon was living in Jerusalem. Simeon was a good man. He loved God and was waiting for God to save the people of Israel. God's Spirit came to him and told him that he would not die until he had seen Christ the Lord.' *Luke 2:25–26*

Tell the story

Jesus was just a little baby when Joseph and Mary took him to the Temple. (The Temple was a big building where people went to worship God, a bit like a church.) Joseph and Mary wanted to say thank you to God for their beautiful baby boy.

At the Temple, a man called Simeon saw them coming. Straight away Simeon knew that Jesus was God's special Son. Simeon held baby Jesus up in his arms and shouted and sang a great big thank you to God.

Then a very old woman called Anna came into the Temple. Anna saw Joseph and Mary with baby Jesus. Straight away, she knew that Jesus was God's special Son. She was so happy! She went all round the Temple telling everyone about Jesus.

Simeon and Anna were both so happy to see the special baby who was God's Son, Jesus.

Talk to God

Thank you, God, that you had told Simeon and Anna that you would be sending your son into the world a long time before he was born.

Use the picture

1 You can use the picture as an introduction to the Bible story or to help you review the story together.

2 There are five Bible-story pictures to go with this series about 'Christmas people', each showing characters who were affected by the news of the coming of Jesus. As the fourth picture is completed (coloured, painted or collaged), tape it to the other scenes ('A message for Mary', 'Jesus is born', 'A message for the shepherds') and keep it to make a long frieze of the whole story.

A message for the wise men

Read it from the Bible

Matthew 2:1–12

'When the men went into the house and saw the child with Mary, his mother, they knelt down and worshipped him. They took out their gifts of gold, frankincense, and myrrh and gave them to him.' *Matthew 2:11*

Tell the story

A long way from Bethlehem, there were some wise men. They were looking at the stars.

"Look at that big, bright star up there," one said.

"It's telling us a king has been born," said another. "How exciting! Let's go and find him."

The wise men chose some special presents to give the baby king. They began a long journey. They followed the star to King Herod's palace. "We've come to see the special baby," they told him.

"What baby?" he asked.

"The new king," the wise men answered.

"But I'm the only king here," said Herod, angrily.

"You will probably find the baby you are looking for in Bethlehem," the king's advisers said. And they were right. The wise men knelt down. They knew Jesus was very special. They gave him the expensive presents they had brought – gold and rich perfumes.

Talk to God

Thank you, God, that you told all sorts of people about the birth of your Son, Jesus!

Use the picture

1 You can use the picture as an introduction to the Bible story or to help you review the story together.

2 There are five Bible-story pictures to go with this series about 'Christmas people', each showing characters who were affected by the news of the coming of Jesus. As the fifth and last picture is completed (coloured, painted or collaged), tape it to the other scenes ('A message for Mary', 'Jesus is born', 'A message for the shepherds', 'Simeon and Anna'). You now have a long frieze of the whole story of Jesus being born.

3 Use the frieze to retell the story, and for the children to tell each other which parts of the story they like best.

A message for the wise men Matthew 2:1–12

Jesus the boy

Read it from the Bible

Luke 2:41–52

'Three days later they found Jesus sitting in the temple, listening to the teachers and asking them questions.' *Luke 2:46*

Tell the story

Jesus and his mum and dad, Mary and Joseph, went to the big city of Jerusalem. They stayed there for a week. When it was time to go home, Mary and Joseph set off, with lots of friends from their village. On the way home, they found out that Jesus was not with them!

Mary and Joseph ran back to Jerusalem. They looked for Jesus all over the place. At last, they found him. He was in the Temple, the beautiful meeting place, where people could go to pray and sing to God. Jesus was talking with the clever men and wise teachers. And Jesus was cleverer than they were!

"Oh, Jesus!" gasped Mary. "We've been so worried about you!"

"This is God's house, my Father's house," said Jesus. "I've been here all the time."

Then they all went home together. And Mary always remembered what Jesus said.

Talk to God

Thank you, God, that it doesn't matter how old we are – you still want us to learn about you.

Use the picture

1 You can use the picture as an introduction to the Bible story or to help you review the story together.

2 Say that one of the people in the picture is Jesus. Can the children work out which one he is? Say that we often hear stories about Jesus when he was grown up, and at Christmas we think about Jesus being born. But this Bible story is about Jesus when he was a boy. It is the only story in the Bible about Jesus as a child. Can the children identify him now?

3 Explain that Jesus knew a lot about God. What questions could Jesus be asking the clever man he is talking to? What might the clever man be asking Jesus?

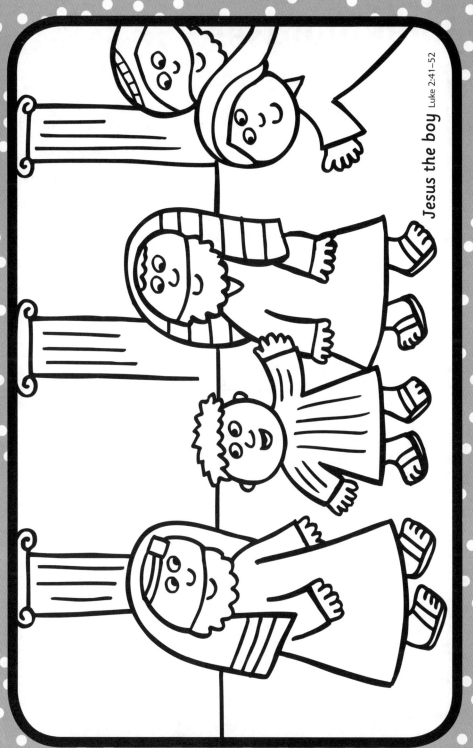

Jesus the boy Luke 2:41–52

John baptises Jesus

Read it from the Bible

Matthew 3:1–17

'"I baptize you with water so that you will give up your sins. But someone more powerful is going to come, and I am not good enough even to carry his sandals. He will baptize you with with the Holy Spirit and with fire."' *Matthew 3:11*

Tell the story

John was calling out to all the people, "Get ready! Get ready! Someone special is coming!"

"Who is coming?" the people asked.

"Someone special is coming from God," replied John.

"How do we have to get ready?" the people asked.

"Say sorry for the wrong things you've done," John told them. "And come to the river and be baptised."

One day, John saw Jesus coming. At once he knew that God had sent that person he had promised. And that person was Jesus!

"Baptise me!" Jesus said to John.

"But you're God's special one," John said. "I can't baptise you."

"It's what God wants just now," Jesus told him.

So John baptised Jesus. Then two special things happened. A beautiful white bird seemed to come and rest on Jesus, to show that the Holy Spirit was there to help Jesus. Then God's gentle voice was heard saying, "Jesus is my own Son. And I am very pleased with him."

Talk to God

Thank you, God, that you forgive us when we say sorry for doing wrong things.

Use the picture

1 You can use the picture as an introduction to the Bible story or to help you review the story together.

2 Describe what is happening in the picture, using the word 'baptise'. Point to John: he has been baptising lots of people. They go into the river and then dip under the water, and come up again. It is a way of showing they are sorry for doing wrong and that they are going to try to live God's way.

3 Jesus has not done anything wrong, so John thinks he does not need to be baptised. But Jesus asks him – and John agrees.

4 Help John to baptise Jesus. First, colour in the picture. Then cut some strips of tissue paper, about 2 x 30 cm. Tape a few strips to the side of the picture, so they can be flipped across the lower part of the page, and cover John and Jesus with 'water'.

John baptises Jesus Matthew 3:1–17

Meeting Jesus

Read it from the Bible

Mark 1:16–20

'Jesus said to them, "Come with me! I will teach you how to bring in people instead of fish."'

Mark 1:17

Tell the story

Peter and his brother Andrew were fishermen. They would stand in the water, with a net. When they saw the fish swimming along, they would throw the net into the water and catch the fish.

One day, they saw a man walking along the beach. It was Jesus.

"Come with me," called Jesus. "Instead of catching fish, come and help me do my work."

Peter and Andrew stopped fishing. They left the nets on the beach. They went with Jesus.

A little way along the shore, James and John were getting ready to go fishing in their boat.

"Come with me," called Jesus. "Instead of catching fish, come and help me do my work."

James and John left their boat. They went with Jesus too.

Peter, Andrew, James and John were very happy they had met Jesus.

Talk to God

Thank you, God, that you ask us to be your friends too.

Use the picture

1 You can use the picture as an introduction to the Bible story or to help you review the story together.

2 Look at the picture together and decide which person is Jesus (on the left), and which is Peter. What do the children think is happening in this picture? (Jesus and Peter are meeting; Jesus is asking Peter to be his friend.) Look at the other items in the picture and work out that Peter's job was fishing. Find a net. Count the fish.

3 Colour in the picture of Jesus. What is he saying to Peter? Use the children's suggestions or all say: 'Hello, Peter. Come with me and be my friend.'

4 If the children think Peter will say 'yes', they can colour him in too. If they think he will say 'no' or if they are not sure, leave him plain. Then listen to today's Bible story and find out what Peter answers. Allow time for children to go back to their pictures and colour in Peter, if they would like to.

Meeting Jesus Mark 1:16–20

Jesus goes to a wedding

Read it from the Bible

John 2:1–11

'Mary then said to the servants, "Do whatever Jesus tells you to do."' John 2:5

Tell the story

What a great party! The wedding was over and the bride and groom's families and friends were enjoying the party food and the wine. Jesus and his mother, Mary, were there too.

Mary was watching everything. She saw jugs of wine being poured out. She saw servants with worried faces. "Jesus," she said. "They've run out of wine to drink." She knew that Jesus would help.

Jesus saw six big stone jars against the wall. He told the servants, "Fill those stone jars with water." Then he said, "Now take some water and give it to the man in charge."

So they filled the stone jars with water. Then they took some water to the man in charge. "Delicious," he said. "That's the best wine I've ever tasted!"

Jesus had turned the water into wine! No ordinary person could do that! But Jesus could because he is God's Son.

Talk to God

Thank you, God, that you want to help all your friends.

Use the picture

1 Use the picture to talk about Jesus and Mary at a wedding party. Ask the children to point out Jesus, Mary, the bride and the groom. Say that Mary noticed the wine was finished and told Jesus. Why do they think she told him? (He cared about his friends and would know what to do to help them.)

2 Say that Jesus told the servants to fill the big stone jars with water. Invite the children to dip their brushes into some water and 'paint' the water jars in their pictures with water.

3 What did Jesus do to the water? He changed it into wine to help his friends! Add red paint or food colouring to the water. Let the children use it to paint the jars again, to show that the water has turned to wine.

4 Encourage the children to complete their pictures. As they work, chat to them about how Jesus also cares for us and helps us.

Jesus goes to a wedding John 2:1–11

An evening visitor

Read it from the Bible

John 3:1–21

'... only God's Spirit can change you into a child of God.' *John 3:6*

Tell the story

Nicodemus was a very clever and important person. Nicodemus had heard about Jesus and the things he was teaching people about God. He wanted to find out for himself if they were true. Nicodemus wanted to ask Jesus lots of questions.

But not everyone liked Jesus. "What if people see me talking to Jesus?" Nicodemus said. "What will they think?"

Nicodemus had an idea. He went to see Jesus secretly one night. "No one will see me when it's dark," he thought.

"I know God has sent you," Nicodemus said to Jesus, "and I know you could not do all the wonderful things you do unless God is with you. But there are some things I don't understand."

Jesus told Nicodemus how much God loves everyone. "You need to become part of God's special family," he said. Then Nicodemus went home.

He had lots to think about.

Talk to God

Thank you, God, that we don't have to talk to you in secret.

Use the picture

1 You can use the picture as an introduction to the Bible story or to help you review the story together.

2 Show the children the Bible-story picture and guide them to identify one of the characters as Jesus. Who could the other person be? What does he look like? Comment on his clothes and the little box on his headband that has words from the Bible inside. Do the children think he looks important?

3 Introduce this second character as Nicodemus and agree that he was an important man. He wanted to talk to Jesus, but he did not want other people to know. So he came to see Jesus at night. How could the children make their pictures look like night-time ones? Help them to think about colours, lights and shadows, before completing their pictures.

An evening visitor John 3:1–21

A woman fetching water

Read it from the Bible

John 4:3–30

'"Come and see a man who told me everything I have ever done! Could he be the Messiah?"'

John 4:29

Tell the story

Jesus was tired. He and his friends had walked a long way. While his friends went into the town to buy food for lunch, Jesus sat down near a well to rest. A woman came to fetch some water. "Please could you give me a drink of water?" Jesus asked. "I'm thirsty."

The woman was very surprised. "People from your country don't usually speak to people from mine," she said.

"You don't know who I am," Jesus told her. "If you did, you would ask me for help. I can give you something far more precious than this water."

Jesus and the woman began to talk.

Jesus had never met her but he knew lots of things about her. "Jesus is amazing," the woman said.

She put down her water jar and ran to tell her friends, "Come and meet Jesus. He knows everything about me."

Talk to God

God, you are amazing! You know every little thing about us. And you still love us, even when we are naughty.

Use the picture

1 You can use the picture as an introduction to the Bible story or to help you review the story together.

2 Look at the Bible-story picture together and identify which character is Jesus. Say that the Bible does not tell us the name of the woman in the picture, just that she came from a country called Samaria.

3 Point to the stones and explain that they are making a wall around a 'well'; a deep hole in the ground with water at the bottom. Explain that this is how people got water to drink, when there were no taps or bottled water.

4 Listen to the Bible story to find out what Jesus and the woman talked out.

A woman fetching water John 4:3–30

A man who needs help

Read it from the Bible

John 4:43–54

'The boy's father realized that at one o'clock the day before, Jesus had told him, "Your son will live!" So the man and everyone in his family put their faith in Jesus.' *John 4:53*

Tell the story

An important man went to see Jesus. The man was very upset. "Please help me," he begged. "My son is very ill. I don't want him to die. Please will you come and make him better?"

"Don't worry. Your son won't die," Jesus told the man. "Go back home and see him." The man began to walk home. It was a long way.

But before the man arrived at his house, he saw some of his servants running to meet him. "Your son is better!" they said, smiling.

"When did that happen?" the man asked.

"Yesterday lunchtime," the servant said. "Suddenly, your son was well again."

"That's exactly the time I asked Jesus to help me," the important man told them. "Jesus promised that my son would get better. Now I believe that Jesus is amazing. He has the power to help people."

Talk to God

Thank you, Jesus, that you made the little boy well again, even though you were a long way away from him and couldn't see him. Thank you that you listen to our prayers too, even though we can't see you either.

Use the picture

1 You can use the picture as an introduction to the Bible story or to help you review the story together.

2 Look at the Bible-story picture and see if you can find Jesus. 'Realise' that he is not there! Explain that Jesus did something very wonderful for the people in this family – but he did it without even going to see them!

3 Find the boy: explain that he was very ill. Find the dad: say that he went a long way to see Jesus to ask him to make his boy well again. The mum stayed with the boy to look after him because he was very ill. Jesus sent the dad back home (pause to colour in the dad). When he got there, his son was well (pause to colour the boy) and everyone was happy (colour the mum).

4 What do the children think about Jesus?

5 You could use this picture, along with the following three, to make a picture book of some of the miracles of Jesus. Get two sheets of thin card, slightly larger than the size of the picture, for each child. Punch holes in the side and tie the pages together with a ribbon to make a simple book. Keep hold of the books and paste a new picture in each time you look at one of the miracle stories.

A man who needs help John 4:43–54

29

A man by the pool

Read it from the Bible

John 5:1–17

'Jesus told him, "Pick up your mat and walk!" At once the man was healed. He picked up his mat and started walking around.' *John 5:8–9*

Tell the story

In a big city called Jerusalem there was a special pool. Lots of people who were ill, who could not see, or could not walk, lay near the edge of the pool and waited. They thought that whenever the water started to bubble, the first person to get into the pool would be made well again. So every day they waited… and waited… and watched the water carefully.

One day, Jesus went to the pool. He saw a man who had been ill for a long, long time. The man could not walk, or wave his arms, or wriggle his toes. "Do you want to be healed?" Jesus asked him.

"Of course I do," answered the man, "but I don't have anyone to help me get into the pool when the water bubbles. So someone else always gets there first."

"Pick up your mat and walk," Jesus told him. And the man did!

Talk to God

Thank you, God, that you care about people and want to make them well. Please make … well too.

Use the picture

1 You can use the picture as an introduction to the Bible story or to help you review the story together.

2 Find Jesus in the picture. Who else is in the scene? Describe what the man is doing. (Standing and carrying a blanket or 'bed'.) Do the children think the man looks well or poorly? Is he happy or sad?

3 While the children complete their pictures, explain that this picture shows the very end of the story. At the start of the story, the man was not very happy and could not walk. Now something has happened: can the children suggest what it could be?

4 You could use this picture, along with the other three in this series, to make a picture book of some of the miracles of Jesus. Use two sheets of thin card, slightly larger than the size of the picture, for each child. Punch holes in the side and tie the pages together with a ribbon to make a simple book. Keep hold of the books and paste a new picture in each time you look at one of the miracle stories.

A man by the pool John 5:1–17

A man who could not walk

Read it from the Bible

Luke 5:17–26

'Everyone was amazed and praised God. What they saw surprised them, and they said, "We have seen a great miracle today!"' *Luke 5:26*

Tell the story

"Let's go and see Jesus!" said the four friends to the man who could not walk. "How will I get there?" he asked. His four friends smiled.

"We'll carry you, of course!"

So the four friends carried him, on a mat, to the house where Jesus was. "Jesus will make things different for you," they told him.

The house was already full of people. "We'll have to go home," said the man.

But the four friends carried him up to the flat roof. They lowered him, still lying on his mat, through the roof right in front of Jesus. Jesus smiled. "The wrong things you've done are forgiven," he said.

The man smiled back. "That makes me feel happy," he thought.

Jesus said, "Get up, pick up your mat and walk."

And that's what the man did! "I can walk!" he shouted. "What a difference Jesus has made to my life!"

Talk to God

Thank you, God, for friends and other people to help us. Thank you for ... Thank you too, that you can do amazing miracles.

Use the picture

1 You can use the picture as an introduction to the Bible story or to help you review the story together.

2 Look at the picture and work out which person is Jesus. Read the caption: 'A man who could not walk'. But the picture shows a man who can walk! What can have happened in the story to make this difference?

3 Listen to the Bible story to find out.

4 Who helped the man? What did they do to help him?

5 You could use this picture, along with the other three in this series, to make a picture book of some of the miracles of Jesus. Use two sheets of thin card, slightly larger than the size of the picture, for each child. Punch holes in the side and tie the pages together with a ribbon to make a simple book. Keep hold of the books and paste a new picture in each time you look at one of the miracle stories.

A man who could not walk Luke 5:17–26

Jesus helps a soldier

Read it from the Bible

Matthew 8:5–13

'Then Jesus said to the officer, "You may go home now. Your faith has made it happen."'

Matthew 8:13

Tell the story

The soldier is very worried. His servant is not very well. He is in bed and he is very ill. The soldier decides to go to Jesus. "Jesus will help," he says.

So he goes to find Jesus.

"Jesus, my servant is ill," he says. "Will you make him better?"

"Of course," says Jesus. "I'll come straight away."

"Oh, you don't need to come," replies the soldier. "Just say the word and my servant will be better. I know that you can do that."

Jesus is very pleased that the soldier trusts him so much. Straight away, Jesus makes the servant well again.

When the soldier goes home, his servant is out of bed and feeling much better.

"I knew Jesus could help," the soldier tells him.

The soldier is right! Jesus will help everyone who asks him.

Talk to God

Thank you, God, for making people well again. Please make .... well.

Use the picture

1 You can use the picture as an introduction to the Bible story or to help you review the story together.

2 Give each child a copy of the picture and read the heading: 'Jesus helps a soldier'. Let the children colour or paint the picture. As they work, chat about the Bible story. Can the children tell you what happened? Who was poorly? Why did the soldier need help? Could Jesus help? What did the soldier think and say? How do the children feel about Jesus?

3 Add the picture to the books. The books should now be finished.

Jesus the storyteller

Read it from the Bible

Matthew 7:24–27

'"Anyone who hears and obeys these teachings of mine is like a wise person who built a house on solid rock."' *Matthew 7:24*

Tell the story

Everyone loved to hear the wonderful stories Jesus told.

One day he told a story about two builders.

The first builder wanted to build a house. He found a great big rock and said, "This is where I will build my house." And he did.

When the house was ready, it began to rain. It rained and rained. The wind blew hard. But the house did not move. It was safe and strong. Just like people who listen carefully to what Jesus says.

The second builder wanted to build a house. He found a beautiful sandy beach and said, "This is where I will build my house." And he did.

When the house was ready, it began to rain. It rained and rained. The wind blew hard.

And do you know what happened?

The house fell down!

Talk to God

Help us, Jesus, to listen to all the things you want to teach us.

Use the picture

1 You can use the picture as an introduction to the Bible story or to help you review the story together.

2 Describe how the two builders made their houses. One took a lot of care and time. The other was quick and did not take so much care. Look at the picture and see if you can work out which house is which.

3 Suggest the children complete their pictures in the same way as the men made their houses. They can be careful and take time with one house; and be quick and rush with the other.

4 Ask each child to look at their own completed picture. Which picture of the house looks better? In Jesus' story, which house was built better when the rain and storm came?

A woman with a gift

Read it from the Bible

Luke 7:36–50

'When a sinful woman in that town found out that Jesus was there, she bought an expensive bottle of perfume. Then she came and stood behind Jesus. She cried and started washing his feet with her tears and drying them with her hair. The woman kissed his feet and poured the perfume on them.' *Luke 7:37–38*

Tell the story

Jesus arrived at Simon's house, feeling hungry and tired. Simon did not welcome him. Simon did not ask his servant to wash Jesus' dusty feet. But he asked Jesus to sit at the table and gave him some food.

While they were eating, a woman came in, carrying a jar of precious perfume. She sat on the floor next to Jesus. She was thinking of the wrong things she had done and how Jesus loved her and forgave her. She began to cry. As her tears fell, she washed Jesus' dusty feet and wiped them with her long hair. She took her precious perfume and gently poured it onto Jesus' feet.

Simon was upset. "Don't you know how bad this woman is?" he asked.

Jesus said, "Simon, when I arrived you didn't welcome me or wash my feet. This woman has given me a wonderful gift. She has shown me how much she loves me."

Talk to God

Thank you, God, that you love every one of us. Thank you that we can say sorry to you and you will forgive us when we have done wrong things.

Use the picture

1 You can use the picture as an introduction to the Bible story or to help you review the story together.

2 Let the children colour or paint their pictures. Assist them to tape long pieces of knitting wool to make hair for the woman. See if the hair is long enough to reach Jesus' feet to wipe them dry.

3 Supervise the children closely while they rub a bar of soap around the edges of the picture or spray very lightly with perfume as a reminder of the gift the woman gave to Jesus.

A woman with a gift Luke 7:36–50

The story of the seeds

Read it from the Bible

Mark 4:1–9

"'But a few seeds did fall on good ground where the plants grew and produced thirty or sixty or even a hundred times as much as was scattered.'" *Mark 4:8*

Tell the story

This is a story Jesus told.

Up and down the field went the farmer.

He threw seeds to one side and more seeds on the other side. Some seeds fell along the path where the soil was hard. Straight away, the birds came swooping down and gobbled them up.

The farmer sowed more seeds. They fell on stony ground. Day after day, they started to grow. But it was so hot and dry on the stony ground that the new plants withered and died.

The farmer sowed more seeds. They fell among tall weeds growing on the edge of the field. Day after day, these seeds grew, but the weeds grew faster than the new plants. And the new plants could not get enough sunlight and died.

The farmer sowed some more seeds. They fell on the good soil where they had plenty of sunlight and water. These seeds grew into good, healthy plants – just what the farmer wanted.

Talk to God

Help us, God, to listen to you carefully, and do what you want us to do.

Use the picture

1 You can use the picture as an introduction to the Bible story or to help you review the story together.

2 Tell the story of the farmer sowing his seeds, as the children colour their pictures.

3 Suggest they add real seeds to their pictures. Help stick on seeds. (Make sure none of the children suffer from seed allergies and choose large seeds that are easy to handle for small fingers. Supervise closely to make sure the seeds go on the picture and not anywhere they shouldn't!) Give some to the farmer to sow and put others on the ground. See if you can be extra careful and make your seeds land on the good soil!

Hidden treasure

Read it from the Bible

Matthew 13:44

"'The kingdom of heaven is like what happens when someone finds treasure hidden in a field and buries it again. A person like that is happy and goes and sells everything in order to buy that field.'" *Matthew 13:44*

Tell the story

"A man was digging in a field...," Jesus began.

"A story!" said his friends. "We love Jesus' stories."

"The man was digging deeper and deeper," Jesus went on. "His spade hit something hard. 'What's this?' the man wondered. He got down on his hands and knees and looked into the hole.

"He saw something shiny. So he dug with his hands and brought out... some treasure! He held it up so that the sun shone on the gold. He stroked it to feel the coolness of the sparkly metal. 'I wish I had treasure like this,' he thought.

"Then he had an idea. He hid the treasure in the field again and went home. He sold everything he had for money. Then he took the money and bought the field from its owner.

"He was very happy. 'Now the treasure is mine!' he said."

Talk to God

Thank you, God, that being part of your family is like having some wonderful treasure!

Use the picture

1 You can use the picture as an introduction to the Bible story or to help you review the story together.

2 This is a picture where you can go wild with collage! Provide a variety of glitter, sequins, plastic 'jewels', cellophane scraps, foil, holographic paper, adhesive shapes and stars, metallic crayons and so on. Set the items out in separate containers and guide the children to choose one piece at a time to stick down on their own 'pile' of treasure.

3 Encourage the children to make their pictures as exciting as they can – just like being part of God's family.

Hidden treasure Matthew 13:44

Jairus and his daughter

Read it from the Bible

Mark 5:21–43

'Then Jesus went inside and said to them, "Why are you crying and carrying on like this? The child isn't dead. She is just asleep."' *Mark 5:39*

Tell the story

Jairus went to find Jesus. "My daughter is dying," Jairus said. "Please will you come and make her well again?"

"Of course," answered Jesus.

Crowds of people followed them as they went to Jairus' house. Everyone wanted to see Jesus. And now it was getting late. Would Jesus be in time to help Jairus' little girl?

Some men ran up to them. "It's too late," they told Jairus. "Your daughter has died." Everyone at his house was crying.

"Don't worry," Jesus said. "Your daughter is only asleep."

Jesus held the girl's hand and said, "Get up." And she did.

Everyone was amazed to see Jairus' daughter walking and running about. But Jesus could do something no one else could. He had healed her.

"I think," said Jesus, smiling at her mummy and daddy, "your little girl might like some food now."

Talk to God

Thank you, God, that you looked after the little girl and made her well, when nobody thought you could. Thank you that you look after us too.

Use the picture

1 You can use the picture as an introduction to the Bible story or to help you review the story together.

2 Give the children the picture of Jesus healing Jairus' daughter. Everyone had thought that the little girl was dead, but now she was alive and well. That's amazing! How do the children think the little girl's mummy and daddy felt when they thought she was dead? How do the children think the mummy and daddy feel now?

3 Provide the children with really bright, happy colours, or collage materials, such as sticky stars, glitter and metallic crayons with which to decorate their pictures.

Jairus and his daughter Mark 5:21–43

Jesus is amazing

Read it from the Bible

Mark 6:45–52

'When the disciples saw Jesus walking on the water, they thought he was a ghost, and they started screaming. All of them saw him and were terrified. But at that same time he said, "Don't worry! I am Jesus. Don't be afraid." He got into the boat with them, and the wind died down. The disciples were completely confused.' Mark 6:49–51

Tell the story

It had been a very busy day for Jesus. He needed to be quiet, so he went to pray. His friends set off across the lake in their little fishing boat.

As they reached the middle of the lake, the wind started to howl round the boat. The little boat rocked on the water. The wind blew stronger than before. Jesus' friends were a little bit scared. They tried to row the boat, but the wind was far too strong.

Suddenly, they saw something. A man was walking on the water! Now they were very scared!

"Don't be afraid," said the man. It was Jesus! He climbed into the boat and told the wind to be still. And it was.

Jesus' friends could see what an amazing person Jesus was.

Talk to God

Thank you, Jesus, for all the amazing things that you did when you lived on earth. Thank you that you still do amazing things today.

Use the picture

1 You can use the picture as an introduction to the Bible story or to help you review the story together.

2 Try some simple experiments with the equipment you have around you, to see what happens when you stand on different surfaces, for example: a carpet, a wooden floor, a blanket, a cushion. Ask the children what would happen if you tried to stand on top of the sea! No one could not do it: they would sink. But it did happen once!

3 Give out the Bible-story pictures and describe the scene together. Make sure the children know that the lower area of the picture is showing water and that the person standing on it is Jesus.

4 Show the children, by your reaction, that this is an amazing thing to be able to do – and that Jesus is an amazing person because he did it.

Jesus is amazing Mark 6:45–52

Jesus feeds many people

Read it from the Bible

Matthew 15:32–39

'His disciples said, "This place is like a desert. Where can we find enough food to feed such a crowd?"' *Matthew 15:33*

Tell the story

Lots of people came to see Jesus. They came to hear the stories Jesus told. They came to see him make sick people well again.

Everyone loved to be with Jesus. No one wanted to go home. They stayed there for one day, two days, then three days. Soon, they had eaten all the food they had brought with them. And soon after that, they began to feel very hungry!

Jesus cared for the people. Jesus knew that they needed food to eat. Jesus' friends had seven loaves of bread and a few fish.

Jesus said, "Thank you," to God for the bread and fish. Then he gave the food to all the people! Lots and lots of people!

And everyone had something to eat. The people could hardly believe it. But they knew they did not have hungry tummies any more.

Just seven loaves of bread and a few fish fed all those people – thanks to Jesus!

Talk to God

Thank you, Jesus, that you know what people need and you look after them. Thank you for looking after us.

Use the picture

1 You can use the picture as an introduction to the Bible story or to help you review the story together.

2 Give each child a copy of the picture and read the heading: 'Jesus feeds many people'. Let the children colour or paint the picture.

3 As the children work, chat about the Bible story. Can the children tell you what happened? Who was hungry? Did they have much food? Could Jesus help? What did Jesus do? What did the people do? How do the children feel about Jesus?

Jesus feeds many people Matthew 15:32–39

Shine, Jesus!

Read it from the Bible

Mark 9:2–13

'... There in front of the disciples, Jesus was completely changed. And his clothes became much whiter than any bleach on earth could make them. Then Moses and Elijah were there talking with Jesus.' Mark 9:2–5

Tell the story

Jesus said to Peter, James and John, "Come with me."

They began to climb a mountain. It was a long way and, by the time they got to the top, Peter, James and John were very tired.

Suddenly, they saw that Jesus looked different! Not tired, like they were. His clothes were bright and shining, not dusty. Even his hands and face and feet seemed to be shining brightly.

Peter, James and John were amazed – and a bit frightened.

A cloud began to swirl round the high mountain. They could see nothing at all except bright, shiny cloud. They heard a voice: "This is my son. I love him very much. Do what he tells you."

It was God's voice!

The cloud drifted away. They could see Jesus again. And now Peter, James and John were sure that Jesus was God's own Son.

Talk to God

Thank you, Jesus, that you are the Son of God, and you really are amazing.

Use the picture

1 You can use the picture as an introduction to the Bible story or to help you review the story together.

2 Let the children colour their pictures with crayons or pencils. Say that they have coloured the pictures well – but that there is something missing. Jesus and his friends (Peter, James and John) all look more-or-less the same – but the Bible story tells us that Jesus suddenly looked very different.

3 Look in your art and craft supplies and see what you can find to make the figure of Jesus really stand out: maybe the children could glue on glitter or sequins; or you have scraps of foil or shiny paper that could be added; or fluorescent paints or pens? Make Jesus as bright and dazzling as you can – and then see how different he looks to the other people in the picture.

Shine, Jesus! Mark 9:2–13

Jesus tells a story

Read it from the Bible

Luke 10:25–37

'Then Jesus asked, "Which one of these three people was a real neighbour to the man who was beaten up by robbers?"' *Luke 10:36*

Tell the story

Jesus often told stories. You can read them in God's book, the Bible.

"One day," began Jesus, "a man set out to walk to Jericho. It was a long and dangerous journey. On the way, some robbers attacked him and took everything he had. The robbers hurt the man and left him lying on the ground. In a while, a priest came along. 'Oh dear,' he thought, 'that man is hurt, but I have important things to do for God. I can't help him.'

"A little later, a lawyer came along. 'Oh dear,' he thought, 'that man is hurt, but I have important things to do for God. I can't help him.'

"A little later, a man from Samaria came along. 'Oh dear,' the Samaritan thought, 'that man is hurt, but he's a Jew who hates us Samaritans.' But all the same, he stopped. He took care of the man and took him somewhere safe.

"Now," said Jesus, "who really did something important for God?"

Talk to God

Thank you, Jesus, for all the wonderful stories you told. Help us to learn from them.

Use the picture

1 You can use the picture as an introduction to the Bible story or to help you review the story together.

2 Let the children colour their pictures. Point to the man who needs help. Let the children dip one fingertip into some paint and press marks on his body to show where he has been hurt.

3 Then help the kind traveller make him better. Place a small piece of fabric over each fingerprint and fix it, with sticky tape. 'Bandage' all the places where he is hurt. Smile: he will soon be better now!

Jesus tells a story Luke 10:25–37

Two friendly sisters

Read it from the Bible

Luke 10:38–42

'The Lord answered, "Martha, Martha! You are worried and upset about so many things, but only one thing is necessary. Mary has chosen what is best, and it will not be taken away from her."' Luke 10:41–42

Tell the story

Mary and Martha were sisters.

One day, Jesus and his friends went to their house.

"Come and have a meal with us," said Martha.

Martha liked cooking. She bustled around, cutting vegetables, making bread and cooking a delicious meal. Martha wanted everything to be just right for Jesus.

Mary sat down with Jesus and his friends. She just wanted to listen to everything Jesus was saying.

Martha got crosser and crosser. "Jesus," she grumbled, "do you think it's fair that I'm doing all this hard work while Mary is sitting doing nothing? Tell her to come and help me."

"Martha," answered Jesus, kindly, "don't get so worried and upset. Of course, I'm pleased you're cooking a lovely meal for us. But Mary knows that I enjoy spending time with my friends too. Leave your work for a while. Come and sit down here with us and talk to me instead."

Talk to God

Thank you, Jesus, that you want to be our friend too, and you love us to spend time with you.

Use the picture

1 You can use the picture as an introduction to the Bible story or to help you review the story together.

2 Can the children work out who is in the picture? Jesus is easy to spot. The other two people are sisters called Martha and Mary. They are both friends of Jesus. Martha is the older sister and Mary is the younger sister. Which person do the children think is Martha? Which is Mary?

3 Jesus often went to their house for dinner and sometimes to stay. Jesus liked being with his friends and they liked being with him.

4 Tell the children why you like spending time with your friend Jesus.

Two friendly sisters Luke 10:38–42

Praying as Jesus did

Read it from the Bible

Matthew 6:8–12; Luke 11:2–4

'… Your Father knows what you need before you ask.' *Matthew 6:8*

Tell the story

Jesus' friends wanted to pray just like Jesus did! But they were never sure what to say to God. So one day they asked, "Jesus, how should we pray?"

"I'll help you," Jesus told them. So Jesus' friends sat down with him and listened.

"When you pray," Jesus said, "talk to God in just the same way as you'd talk to someone who loves you and cares for you – a mother or father or someone else who looks after you. You wouldn't worry about talking to your dad or your mum. Just say how you feel. Ask for things you need. Tell God you love him. Thank him for what he's given you. You can say you're sorry too for anything you've done that was wrong. Your Father in heaven loves you and knows just what you need."

And Jesus taught them a prayer to say. It begins, "Our Father in heaven…"

Talk to God

Thank you, God, that we can talk to you like we would talk to a mum or dad or someone else who looks after us. You are so kind, and you know everything that we need.

Use the picture

1 You can use the picture as an introduction to the Bible story or to help you review the story together.

2 Give out the story pictures to the children. Tell them that the person in the picture is Jesus. How does Jesus look? (Happy and trusting.)

3 Read the story together. How does Jesus say we should talk to God? (Like someone we love and trust: a mum or dad, or someone else who looks after us and loves us.)

4 Set out an area of the room as a 'prayer corner'. Make the area comfortable, with cushions and rugs to sit on. Provide things to look at, admire and handle.

5 Encourage the children to colour or decorate the picture in the prayer corner. Provide a calm atmosphere, with some soothing music playing softly in the background.

Praying as Jesus did Matthew 6:8–12; Luke 11:2–4

A woman with a bad back

Read it from the Bible

Luke 13:10–17

'When Jesus saw the woman, he called her over and said, "You are now well." He placed his hands on her, and at once she stood up straight and praised God.' *Luke 13:12–13*

Tell the story

Jesus was in the meeting place where people went to talk to God. Lots of other people were there too. They were listening to Jesus telling them about God.

One of the people listening was a woman. She had a bad back. For years and years, her back had hurt so much that she could not stand up straight.

Jesus saw the woman and he knew what was wrong. Jesus said, "You are well, now!"

Then Jesus put his hands on her shoulders. Her back grew straight and she lifted her head and looked at Jesus!

"Thank you, oh, thank you!" she laughed happily. "God is so wonderful! He's good and kind and loving. And he has made me well!"

Talk to God

Thank you, Jesus, that you made the woman with the bad back better. Thank you that you care all about us, and want us to be well.

Use the picture

1 You can use the picture as an introduction to the Bible story or to help you review the story together.

2 Look at the picture and identify the two characters. Which one is Jesus? Who is the other person? What has Jesus just done?

3 Remember that the woman's back hurt, so she could not move around very easily. What would that be like? Try colouring your pictures in an awkward way: you could try using your non-preferred hand, or lying on the floor, not looking at the page while you are colouring, or bent over, as the woman was. Make it as difficult as possible but keep this light-hearted: the idea is to see that lack of movement affects how we do things. What are the pictures like?

4 Now try completing the pictures in the normal way. (Have spare copies available if the children want a clean picture.) Is it easier? What are the pictures like, now? What was the woman like, when Jesus made her back better?

A woman with a bad back Luke 13:10–17

Come to the party

Read it from the Bible

Luke 14:15–24

'His master then told him, "Go out along the back roads and lanes and make people come in, so that my house will be full."' *Luke 14:23*

Tell the story

This is a story that Jesus told.

A man was getting ready for a party. He had asked all his friends.

When the party was ready, he said to his helper, "Go and tell my friends to come now."

The helper asked all the friends to come. But they all said, "We're too busy to come to the party now!"

So the helper went back to the man and said, "No one can come. They're all too busy."

The man was upset. "My party is ready," he said. "I want lots of people to come." So he sent his helper out again to find poor people, hurt people, sad people, people with no homes.

"Come to the party!" he said. And they did! The man was happy now. His house was full and everyone was enjoying the party.

Talk to God

Thank you, God, that you want us all to be your friends and to join you for your great party in heaven.

Use the picture

1 You can use the picture as an introduction to the Bible story or to help you review the story together.

2 Colour or decorate the elements of the picture as you tell the Bible story.

3 First there was a man who wanted all his friends to come to a party. The man got ready for the party. There was plenty of food to eat. It all looked lovely. And, at last, people came to the party. Everyone had a great time.

4 Look at the completed pictures. Which part of the feast looks best? Pretend to pick up the food from the table and eat it: does it taste good? Is it fun being at God's party?

Come to the party Luke 14:15–24

61

The lost sheep

Read it from the Bible

Luke 15:1–7

'Jesus said, "In the same way there is more happiness in heaven because of one sinner who turns to God than over ninety-nine good people who don't need to."' *Luke 15:7*

Tell the story

A shepherd had lots of sheep. He always counted them as they went into the sheepfold. But one night, a sheep was missing. The shepherd counted again. "98... 99..." Oh dear! The shepherd knew he should have one hundred sheep. What was he going to do?

The shepherd made sure the other sheep were safe. Then he went to search for the lost one. He looked behind walls, he looked near the stream, but he could not find the sheep.

He searched in bushes and he scrambled over rocks, but he still could not find it.

The shepherd climbed higher up the hillside. He walked along stony paths until he heard a quiet, "Baaa!" sound. The shepherd was so happy. At last, he had found his lost sheep. He lifted it onto his shoulders and carried it safely home.

The shepherd thought all his sheep were special.

God thinks we are all special too.

Talk to God

Thank you, God, that each one of us is very special to you, and you love us very much.

Use the picture

1 You can use the picture as an introduction to the Bible story or to help you review the story together.

2 Let the children describe what they can see in the picture. Help them become familiar with words like 'sheep' and 'shepherd'.

3 The picture lends itself to a collage activity. Give texture to the sheep with knitting wool or cotton wool. The shepherd could have a rough coat to keep him warm as he works outside. You could add some of the rest of the flock to the picture as the shepherd returns home.

4 As each child completes their picture, comment that the shepherd is happy to have found his lost sheep.

A loving father

Read it from the Bible

Luke 15:11–24

'The younger son got up and started back to his father. But when he was still a long way off, his father saw him and felt sorry for him. He ran to his son and hugged and kissed him.' *Luke 15:20*

Tell the story

A father had two sons. He loved them very much. Was he happy? (**Yes!**)

The younger son decided to leave home. Was he happy? (**Yes!**)

The father missed his son. Was he happy now? (**No!**) He was sad.

The son was having a good time spending all his money. Was he happy? (**Yes!**)

Then one day all his money was gone. Was he happy now? (**No!**) He was sad. The son was poor and hungry. Was he happy now? (**No!**) He was very sad.

"I'm going to go home," said the son. "I know my father will be cross with me. But he might give me a job." Was the son happy now? (**No!**)

The father saw his son coming along the road. The father ran to meet his son. Was the father sad? (**No!**) Was he cross? (**No!**) Was he happy? (**Yes!**)

The father hugged his son. He was so happy his son was back home because he loved him very much.

Talk to God

Thank you, God, that you love us even when we've done naughty things.

Use the picture

1 You can use the picture as an introduction to the Bible story or to help you review the story together.

2 While the children complete their pictures, talk about the dad and son in the Bible story. On the picture, you can see that they love each other. Jesus told the story to help people know that God loves us.

3 Chat about how people show love by drawing 'x' kisses on a letter or card. Suggest the children decorate all around their pictures with kisses to show God's love for us.

Jesus and the children

Read it from the Bible

Mark 10:13–16

'... "Let the children come to me! Don't try to stop them. People who are like these little children belong to the kingdom of God."' *Mark 10:14*

Tell the story

"We're going to see Jesus!" the children were calling to everyone they saw. "We're going to see Jesus!" they told their mums and dads.

"Yes, isn't it exciting?" their parents said. "We're nearly there."

The children raced on, looking forward to seeing Jesus, who was so kind and who told such wonderful stories! But before they could reach Jesus, they met some men who frowned at them. The men shouted to the mums and dads, "Take the children away! Jesus is too busy to see them!"

The children stood still. They were very disappointed. But Jesus saw what was happening. He stopped what he was doing. Jesus called to the men, "Don't stop the children. They are very special. I always have time for them."

Then Jesus stretched out his arms and the children ran to him. Jesus prayed for them and talked to them. The children felt happy because Jesus wanted to see them.

Talk to God

Thank you, God, that you really love children and want us to get to know you.

Use the picture

1 You can use the picture as an introduction to the Bible story or to help you review the story together.

2 Look at the picture of the children going to Jesus. Ask the children, 'Which child would you like to be?' Let them colour in that child.

3 Ask, 'Who are you going to see?' 'What does he say to you?' 'Is he pleased to see you?' Let them colour in Jesus.

4 Say that each and every child is loved by God. Colour in all the other children in the picture – because Jesus welcomes all children!

Jesus the friend

Read it from the Bible

Luke 19:1–10

'When Jesus got there, he looked up and said, "Zacchaeus, hurry down! I want to stay with you today." Zacchaeus hurried down and gladly welcomed Jesus.' *Luke 19:5–6*

Tell the story

Zacchaeus was a very small man.

He was the smallest person in the whole village.

One day, Jesus came to his village. Lots of people came to see him. Zacchaeus was very excited about seeing Jesus too. But Zacchaeus could not see because he was too small. All the people in the crowd were taller than him. What could he do?

Just then he looked up, saw a tree and had an idea. Quickly, Zacchaeus climbed up the tree to see Jesus.

Jesus came into the village and saw all the crowds. As he walked along he looked up, saw the tree and – what a surprise! There was Zacchaeus! "Come down," said Jesus. "I want to come to your house. I want to be your friend."

Quickly, Zacchaeus climbed down the tree to see Jesus.

Jesus went to Zacchaeus' house.

And Zacchaeus became Jesus' friend.

Talk to God

Thank you, God, that you know all about us and you want to be our friend.

Use the picture

1 You can use the picture as an introduction to the Bible story or to help you review the story together.

2 Chat about all the places where you meet and make friends, such as nursery, school, church, your group, at gym club and so on. Ask if anyone has met a friend when they were up in a tree!

3 Give out the Bible-story pictures and explain that this is what happened to Jesus and Zacchaeus. Zacchaeus was up in a tree, trying to see Jesus. Jesus saw him and asked him to come down – and very soon they were friends!

Palm Sunday

Read it from the Bible

Mark 11:1–11

'The disciples led the donkey to Jesus. They put some of their clothes on its back, and Jesus got on. Many people spread clothes on the road, while others went to cut branches from the fields.' Mark 11:7–8

Tell the story

Jesus was walking to a big city called Jerusalem. He told two of his friends, "Please go into that village over there. You will see a young donkey tied up near a gate. Untie it and bring it to me."

"But what if someone asks what we're doing?" they asked.

"Just tell them that I need to borrow their donkey," Jesus said.

So the men went to find it. They put coats over the donkey's back to make it more comfortable for Jesus to sit on.

Jesus rode the donkey into Jerusalem. People cheered and laid their coats on the ground to make a carpet. They cut branches from the palm trees at the side of the road and waved them in the air as the procession passed. "Hooray for Jesus," everybody shouted. "Hooray for the special King God promised to send us."

Talk to God

Thank you, Jesus, that you are our friend as well as a special king.

Use the picture

1 Use the picture to help you review the story together. Provide each child with a copy of the picture and ask them to tell you who is in it. Give them plenty of time to colour their picture of Jesus and the donkey.

2 When all the pictures are complete, look at them together and chat about the events of the story.

3 Point out that the pictures all show Jesus and a donkey. Why is Jesus getting on the donkey? Can anyone remember where he was going to on the donkey? What happened when Jesus rode into Jerusalem? What did the people shout out? What did they wave? Encourage all the children to contribute answers.

4 Look at the pictures again and ask the children to cheer and wave, as the people in the crowd did. Explain that we can feel just as excited today because Jesus is our friend: cheer and wave again!

A meal with Jesus

Read it from the Bible

Luke 22:7–23

'Jesus took some bread in his hands and gave thanks for it. He broke the bread and handed it to his apostles. Then he said, "This is my body, which is given for you. Eat this as a way of remembering me!" Luke 22:19

Tell the story

"It's Passover," Jesus told his friends.

"Time for our special meal."

When the meal was ready, Jesus said, "This is the last Passover meal we will all eat together. Soon, some sad things are going to happen."

Jesus held a cup of wine in his hands. "Thank you, God," he said. Then Jesus gave the cup to his friends. "Pass this round and all have a drink from it," he said.

Next, Jesus held a loaf of bread and broke it into pieces. "Thank you, God," he said, and gave it to his friends. "When you eat this," he told them, "I want you to think about me."

After their meal, Jesus held another cup of wine in his hands.

"Share this," he said. "Soon someone in this room will choose not to be my friend any more."

His friends looked at each other, amazed. "Who is it?" they wondered.

Talk to God

Thank you, Jesus, that we can think of you when we eat and drink.

Use the picture

1 You can use the picture as an introduction to the Bible story or to help you review the story together.

2 Look at the picture and work out what is going on. Identify which person is Jesus. Who are the other people? What are they all doing? What is Jesus holding? Why? Explain that this was an important meal. Jesus and his friends are sharing it together. It is a meal held once a year called the 'Passover' meal.

3 Ask the children to find the bread and colour it in (or stick on pieces of brown paper). Jesus shared the bread with his friends. He asked them to think about him when they ate bread.

4 Jesus is holding a cup. Let the children colour or decorate it. Jesus shared the drink with his friends. He asked them to think about him when they drank.

5 Suggest that the children could think about Jesus next time they eat or drink, just like Jesus' friends did.

A meal with Jesus Luke 22:7–23

Peter lets Jesus down

Read it from the Bible
Mark 14:27–31,66–72

'Jesus replied, "This very night before a cock crows twice, you will say three times that you don't know me."' *Mark 14:30*

Tell the story

"Jesus, I will always be your friend," said Peter. Jesus was sad.

"Tomorrow," he said, "before the cockerel crows for a new day, you will have said three times that you don't know me."

"No!" replied Peter. "I would never say that!"

That night, some soldiers came and took Jesus away. Peter went to see what was happening.

"You're a friend of Jesus, aren't you?" asked a girl.

Peter was frightened. "No, I'm not," he whispered.

The girl told a man, "I'm sure he's a friend of Jesus."

"No, I'm not!" said Peter.

"Are you a friend of Jesus?" asked the man.

"NO! I'm not!" insisted Peter.

Cock-a-doodle-doo! The cockerel crowed! It was a new day.

And Peter remembered what Jesus had said! Peter felt so sad – he loved Jesus but he had pretended he did not know him!

Talk to God

Thank you, God, that you know all about us, but you still love us!

Use the picture

1 You can use the picture as an introduction to the Bible story or to help you review the story together.

2 This picture lends itself to collage, using real feathers or shaped tissue or crêpe paper to cover the cockerel with bright plumage. If you enlarge the picture, you could make a life-size (or larger than life-size!) bird.

3 Have the children heard a real cockerel or hen sound? They often make loud crowing noises early in the morning, even before it is daylight! Try making some noisy cockerel sounds together!

4 Suggest the children listen out for a cockerel as you tell today's Bible story.

Peter lets Jesus down Mark 14:27-31,66-72

Easter Sunday

Read it from the Bible

Mark 16:1–8

'The man said, "Don't be alarmed! You are looking for Jesus from Nazareth, who was nailed to a cross. God has raised him to life, and he isn't here. You can see the place where they put his body. Now go and tell his disciples and especially Peter, that he will go ahead of you to Galilee. You will see him there, just as he told you."' *Mark 16:6–7*

Tell the story

Early one morning, just as the sun was beginning to rise in the sky, Mary and her friends went to the cave where Jesus had been buried. They were feeling very upset that Jesus had died. The women knew that there was a huge stone in front of the cave. "How are we going to move it?" they wondered.

But when they reached the cave, they could not believe their eyes. The heavy stone had been rolled away from the doorway. They saw a man in white clothes.

"What's happened?" they wondered.

"Please don't be afraid," the man told them. "Jesus isn't here any more. Have a look for yourselves. Jesus isn't dead. He's alive. Go back and tell all his other friends what's happened."

Mary and her friends were amazed and excited by the wonderful news. They were so happy that Jesus was alive again!

Talk to God

Thank you, Jesus, that you came back to life again after you had died – that's amazing!

Use the picture

1 You can use the picture as an introduction to the Bible story or to help you review the story together.

2 Decorate the picture of the cave on Easter morning. The character in front of the cave is an angel: can the children make the angel extra bright and shiny?

3 Talk about the Easter story. Was Jesus in the cave? No! What is the angel saying? Jesus is alive!

4 Turn the paper over and draw a picture of Jesus.

5 Turn the pictures into flags by taping one short edge to a length of bamboo cane. Wave your flags. Now everyone can see Jesus is alive again!

Easter Sunday Mark 16:1–8

Friends again

Read it from the Bible

John 21:15–19

'When Jesus and his disciples had finished eating, he asked, "Simon son of John, do you love me more than the others do?"' *John 21:15*

Tell the story

Peter was very sad because he had said Jesus was not his friend. Then something even more terrible happened. Jesus was killed. He was dead and Peter could not tell him how sorry he was and that he still wanted to be friends. Then God did something wonderful! Jesus was alive again!

Peter and Jesus' other friends went fishing. Jesus met them on the seashore and they all had breakfast together. They were all so happy that Jesus was alive. But could Peter and Jesus be friends again?

Jesus asked Peter, "Do you love me?"

"Yes!" said Peter.

Jesus asked again, "Do you love me?"

"Yes!" said Peter.

Three times Jesus asked, "Do you love me?"

And three times Peter said, "Yes!"

Jesus smiled, "I still need you to help me do God's work."

Now Peter knew that Jesus loved him and still wanted him as a very special friend.

Talk to God

Thank you, Jesus, that you always give us a second chance.

Use the picture

1 You can use the picture as an introduction to the Bible story or to help you review the story together.

2 Look at the Bible-story picture and identify Jesus (on the left) and Peter. Say, 'I wonder what they are talking about?' What do the children think?

3 Remind them that Peter had let Jesus down. Peter said he was not a friend of Jesus – but look again at the picture. Do they look friendly here? Agree that they do and show that you are pleased that they are friends again. But what can have happened?

4 Read the Bible story or tell it in your own words, while the children complete their pictures.

Friends again John 21:15–19

Jesus to Heaven

Read it from the Bible

Luke 24:50–53; Acts 1:1–11

'After Jesus had said this and while they were watching, he was taken up into a cloud. They could not see him, but as he went up, they kept looking up into the sky.' *Acts 1:9–10*

Tell the story

"I am going away soon," Jesus said.

"Where are you going?" his friends asked.

"I'm going back to live with Father God in heaven," Jesus replied.

"What about us?" they asked.

"Wait in Jerusalem," Jesus told them. "I won't be with you, but I will send someone else to help you. Remember the job I've given you to do. Tell everyone, everywhere, that I am alive."

Jesus prayed for his friends.

Then Jesus left them. His friends looked up at the sky until they could not see him any more.

Suddenly, two messengers from God appeared. "Jesus has gone," they told his friends, "but one day you will see him again."

The friends felt happy. Although they could not see Jesus any more, in a special way he was still with them.

Just as he is with us.

Talk to God

Jesus you are just amazing!

Use the picture

1 Provide each child with a copy of the picture of Jesus going to heaven. Talk about what is happening in the picture. How amazing that Jesus has come alive again and now is going back to heaven where he will be always. Let the children colour their pictures if they wish.

2 Admire the pictures and then comment that the scene shows a very special event. Is there anything else you could do, to make the pictures show this even more?

3 Provide a selection of glitter and shiny shapes. Help the children to put glue around Jesus and sprinkle with glitter or add shiny shapes. As they do so, talk with them about how amazing it is that Jesus came back to life and then went to heaven. Would the children like to have been there?

Jesus goes to heaven Luke 24:50–53; Acts 1:1–11

Early one morning

Read it from the Bible

John 14:15–16; Acts 2:1–4

'Suddenly there was a noise from heaven like the sound of a mighty wind! It filled the house where they were meeting. Then they saw what looked like fiery tongues moving in all directions, and a tongue came and settled on each person there. The Holy Spirit took control of everyone, and they began speaking whatever languages the Spirit let them speak.' *Acts 2:2–4*

Tell the story

One day, Jesus said to his friends, "I am going away soon, but God will send someone else who will always be with you."

The friends waited in Jerusalem. They wondered when this person would come. What would he be like?

A few weeks later, lots of Jesus' friends were together in a room. Suddenly, they heard a noise like a strong wind blowing. They could hear it all around them. Something special was happening. Next, the friends saw what looked like flames dancing above people's heads. But they were not hot like ordinary flames.

Then they all started talking in lots of different languages. People from other countries were amazed because they could all understand what the friends were saying.

Then Jesus' friends knew that God had sent his Holy Spirit to help them. The Holy Spirit was the person Jesus had promised would always be with them.

Talk to God

Thank you, God, that you sent your Holy Spirit to us.

Use the picture

1 You can use the picture as an introduction to the Bible story or to help you review the story together.

2 Set out low tables with a range of crayons, pencils and pens. Give each child a picture and encourage them to apply the colours.

3 Begin to tell the story from Acts 2, building a sense of expectation. What is going to happen? What does it mean? Suddenly, there is a sound like a wind blowing. Pick up a picture and wave it in the wind! Then something like flames appears.

4 The friends of Jesus wanted to tell everyone about him. Pick up the pictures again and walk around with them above your heads. Tell other people that Jesus loves them.

Early one morning John 14:15–16; Acts 2:1–4

Walking, leaping and praising God

Read it from the Bible

Acts 3:1–10

'... At once the man's feet and ankles became strong, and he jumped up and started walking. He went with Peter and John into the temple, walking and jumping and praising God.' *Acts 3:7–8*

Tell the story

Peter and John were going to the Temple to pray.

They saw a man sitting near the door. He could not walk. His friends carried him there every day.

The man held out a bowl. He hoped Peter and John would give him some money to buy food. Peter said, "I'm sorry. I don't have any money but I can give you something else."

Peter told the man, "Trust us. In the name of Jesus, get up and walk."

The man wiggled his toes, and moved his ankles. His legs did not feel wobbly any more. They felt strong.

The man stood up. "Look!" he shouted. "I can walk!"

Everybody wanted to know what had happened. "Aren't you the man who always sits by the Temple door?" they asked.

"Yes," he said, laughing, "but just look at me now!"

Peter explained, "God gave us the power to make him well."

Talk to God

Thank you, God, for sending your Holy Spirit to heal people.

Use the picture

1 You can use the picture as an introduction to the Bible story or to help you review the story together.

2 Begin the story, with everyone sitting or crouching on the floor and each holding a copy of the picture of the man who has been healed.

3 When the man starts to leap, walk and praise God, all jump up and hold the pictures high in the air!

Walking, leaping and praising God Acts 3:1–10

Philip

Read it from the Bible

Acts 8:26–40

'The Lord's angel said to Philip, "Go south along the desert road that leads from Jerusalem to Gaza." So Philip left ...' Acts 8:26–27

Tell the story

Philip was one of Jesus' friends. One day an angel told him,

"Go to a road near Jerusalem." Philip did not know why he had to go there, but he did what the angel said.

Philip saw an important man riding in a chariot. He was reading.

"Hurry up," said God. "Go and talk to him."

Philip did not know why he had to talk to the man, but he did what God told him. "Do you understand what you're reading?" Philip asked.

"No," the man answered. "I'd like some help."

Philip climbed into the chariot. The man was reading about a special person God was going to send. "That person is Jesus," Philip told him.

"I'd like to be a friend of Jesus," the man said. So Philip told the man all about Jesus. Now he knew why God had sent him to that place.

Talk to God

Thank you, God, that you give us people who can help us to understand your book, the Bible.

Use the picture

1 Use the activity after telling the Bible story. Look together at the picture and identify the man from Africa in the chariot and Philip talking to him. Ask the children what the African man has been doing and point to the scroll he is holding.

2 Show the children a Bible and say that some of the same words in your Bible were in the scroll the man was reading. He was reading about Jesus and wanted to know more!

3 As the children colour the picture, talk about the chariot and horse, discussing how people travel without cars and other machines with engines!

4 When the children have finished, take the Bible and read a short passage about Jesus. Mark 10:13–16 would be suitable. Before reading say that you are going to find out something about Jesus by reading the Bible – just as the African man did.

Philip Acts 8:26—40

Peter

Read it from the Bible

Acts 12:4–17

'Suddenly an angel from the Lord appeared, and light flashed around in the cell. The angel poked Peter in the side and woke him up. Then he said, "Quick! Get up!" Acts 12:7

Tell the story

King Herod did not like Peter telling everybody about Jesus.

He put Peter in prison.

The king told his soldiers, "Put chains on Peter's hands and feet! Guard all the doors! Don't let him escape."

But Peter's friends in the Jesus family were praying that God would look after Peter – and God did!

One night, when Peter was asleep, a bright light suddenly shone. The chains fell off Peter's arms and legs. "Wake up and get dressed quickly," an angel said. Peter did what he was told. The angel led Peter past all the soldiers and out of the prison. At first, Peter thought he was dreaming. He went to the house where he knew his friends were praying. "Open the door!" he shouted. "It's me, Peter."

Then everybody knew that God had looked after Peter, just as they had asked him to.

Talk to God

Thank you, God, that you look after us and answer our prayers.

Use the picture

1 The activity can be done after telling the Bible story. Give out the pictures face down so the children see a blank piece of paper. Ask them to think about how Peter and his friends felt when he was in prison. They can draw a face with an appropriate expression on the paper.

2 Turn over the paper and find Peter in the picture. Ask the children who Peter is talking to. Where are they? Help them to see that Peter is talking to an angel. The angel has come to get him out of prison.

3 Let the children colour the picture, encouraging them to make the angel look special, perhaps by glueing shiny paper on the angel's clothes. Say that the angel is special because he was sent by God to get Peter out of prison. God had heard the prayers of Peter's friends. How did they feel then?

Peter Acts 12:4-17

Paul and Silas

Read it from the Bible
Acts 16:23–40

'About midnight Paul and Silas were praying and singing praises to God, while the other prisoners listened. Suddenly a strong earthquake shook the jail to its foundations. The doors opened, and the chains fell from all the prisoners.' Acts 16:25–26

Tell the story

In a dark, damp prison cell sat Paul and Silas. They had not done anything wrong. All they had done was tell people about Jesus. Some people did not like this, so they had put them in prison.

Paul and Silas were chained up, but they spent all night praying and singing to God. Suddenly, the prison cell began to shake. The doors to the prison flew open. Paul and Silas' chains fell off. The chains fell off the other prisoners too. The jailer woke up with a jump. He saw what was happening and he was very afraid.

Paul and Silas saw this. "Don't worry," they said. "All the prisoners are still here."

The jailer realised that Paul and Silas were good people. He knew that they had been set free because they were friends of Jesus. He asked Paul and Silas to tell all his family about God's love. That night the jailer and all his family became friends of Jesus.

Talk to God

Thank you, God, that you look after us in amazing ways!

Use the picture

1 You can use the picture as an introduction to the Bible story or to help you review the story together.

2 Here is Paul again in today's Bible-story picture. But where is he this time? He has been put into prison, not because he has been naughty, but because he has been telling people about Jesus. Can Paul still tell people about Jesus when he is in prison? Yes, he can! Paul's friend Silas is with him (although we can't see him in the picture) and they are both singing to God and praying – and the other prisoners and the man who is in charge can hear them.

3 Look more closely at the picture. What has happened? Pick up the paper and shake it, like an earthquake! The prison is falling down, but Paul and Silas do not run away and escape. They stay and tell the man in charge how he can be a friend of Jesus, just like they are.

4 Stop the earthquake so you can decorate the pictures! Then help Paul and Silas tell the good news: 'Jesus loves you and he wants to be your friend.' What will the man in charge say? 'Yes!'

Paul and Silas Acts 16:23–40

Paul in danger

Read it from the Bible
Acts 23:12–33

'When Paul's nephew heard about the plot, he went to the fortress and told Paul about it.'

Acts 23:16

Tell the story

Paul's nephew was worried.

He had heard that some nasty men wanted to hurt Uncle Paul.

"What can I do?" wondered Paul's nephew. "How can I help Uncle Paul?"

He went to see the man in charge of the Roman soldiers.

"Please, sir," he said, "some men are going to hurt my Uncle Paul."

"I will stop them," promised the man in charge. "Leave it with me."

Late at night, when it was dark, the man in charge told his soldiers to get a horse for Paul to ride. Then all the soldiers lined up with Paul, some in front, some behind, some on one side, some on the other. They took Paul far away to a safe place where the nasty men could not hurt him.

God had kept Paul safe.

Talk to God

Thank you, God, that you looked after Paul and that you look after us too.

Use the picture

1 You can use the picture as an introduction to the Bible story or to help you review the story together.

2 Use your voice to give a sense of urgency to the Bible story. Paul is in danger but, thanks to his nephew, he is being taken to safety. It is happening at night time. Chat with the children about how to make their pictures show it is night. (You might need some sticky stars to help with this.) Then let the children get to work!

Paul talks about Jesus

Read it from the Bible

Acts 26:12–32

'But before they left, they said, "This man isn't guilty of anything. He doesn't deserve to die or to be put in jail."' *Acts 26:31*

Tell the story

Paul was a prisoner. He was taken to see the king. His name was Agrippa. Lots of important people were there as well. "What have you done wrong?" asked King Agrippa.

"Nothing," said Paul. "I talk to people and tell them about Jesus. Some people did not like me talking about Jesus. So I was put in prison."

"Well," said King Agrippa, "tell me about Jesus."

So Paul told the king about how he had once been on a journey. "Suddenly," Paul said, "I saw a bright light. It shone in my eyes. I couldn't see anybody or anything. Jesus spoke to me. Since then, I have changed. Once I didn't like people who followed Jesus. Now I am a friend of Jesus myself. And I want everyone else to be friends of Jesus too."

King Agrippa wondered if what Paul said about Jesus was true.

Talk to God

Thank you, God, that you are so amazing. It's good to tell other people about how amazing you are!

Use the picture

1 You can use the picture as an introduction to the Bible story or to help you review the story together.

2 Help the children to identify who is in the picture. Paul is doing what he always does: he is talking about Jesus.

3 Complete the picture and then think about what Paul is saying, perhaps, 'Jesus loves you and wants to be your friend.' What stories could Paul tell about Jesus? Encourage the children to think of a story they know and to tell it to each other now.

First steps in Bible reading

The *Tiddlywinks* range of Little Books

My Little Red Book
First steps in Bible reading
Reese discovers Christmas is coming...
978 1 85999 659 1

My Little Yellow Book
First steps in Bible reading
Danny finds out about Easter.
978 1 85999 693 5

My Little Blue Book
First steps in Bible reading
Lucy and Liam find out about me...
978 1 85999 660 7

My Little Green Book
First steps in Bible reading
Krista explores God's wonderful world
978 1 85999 696 6

My Little Purple Book
First steps in Bible reading
Lily discovers 'Jesus loves me'.
978 1 85999 720 8

My Little Orange Book
First steps in Bible reading
Jamie looks inside God's book.
978 1 85999 717 8

Tiddlywinks Little Books are designed to be used at home by a parent/carer with an individual child. Linked to the themes covered in the *Tiddlywinks* Big Books, children can discover and learn about the Bible and share their discoveries with you. There are 50 first steps in Bible reading pages in each book, with a story for each day and extra activity pages of fun things to do. Children will love exploring the Bible with child characters Lucy and Liam, Reese, Danny, Krista, Lily and Jamie.
A5, 64pp £3.50 each (Prices subject to change)

You can order these or any other *Tiddlywinks* resources from:

- Your local Christian bookstore
- Scripture Union Mail Order:
  Telephone 01908 856006
- Online: log on to
  www.scriptureunion.org.uk/tiddlywinks
  to order securely from our online bookshop

> **"** When the Big Books are use in conjunction with the Little Boo, children and adults encounter an attractive mixture of stories and activities that will encourage everybody to know and trust in Jesus. **"**
> **Diana Turner,**
> **Editor of Playleader Magazine**

Tiddlywinks
The flexible resource for pre-school children and carers

Also now on sale
Say and Sing. Glitter and Glue. Make and D